English

Pre-school Series

PRACHI

CURSIVE CAPITAL LETTERS

Prachi Tyagi

Prachi [India] Pvt. Ltd.

SMART BOOKS FOR SMART LEARNING

Date : _____

Sign. : _____

☆☆☆☆☆

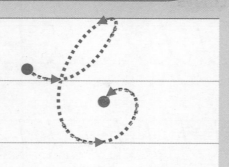

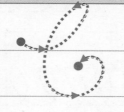

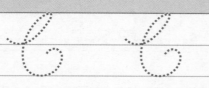

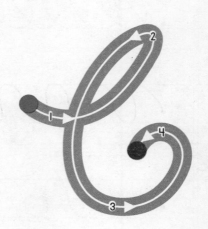

Now, write the letter $\mathcal{C}$.

Date : _____   Sign. : _____   ☆☆☆☆☆

CAR

𝒞   𝒞   𝒞   𝒞   𝒞

Date : _____

Sign. : _____

☆☆☆☆☆

EGG

Now, write the letter $\mathcal{E}$.

Date : _____   Sign. : _____   ☆ ☆ ☆ ☆ ☆

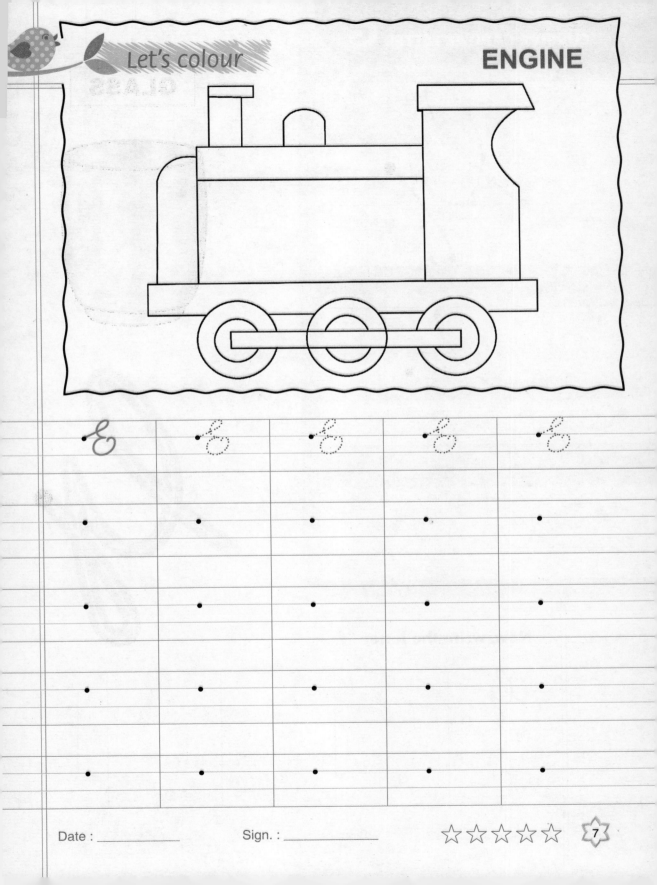

GLASS

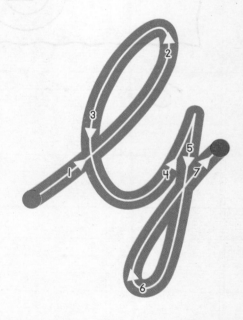

Now, write the letter $\mathcal{G}$.

Date : _____   Sign. : _____   ☆☆☆☆☆

Let's colour

GOAT

Date : _____   Sign. : _____

ICE-CREAM

Now, write the letter $\mathcal{I}$.

Date : _____   Sign. : _____   ☆ ☆ ☆ ☆ ☆

𝒢   𝓰   𝓰   𝓰   𝓰

Date : _____   Sign. : _____   ☆☆☆☆☆

JAM

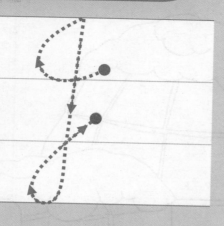

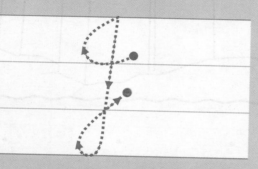

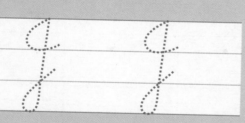

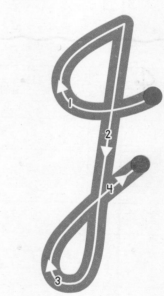

Now, write the letter *J* .

Date : _____

Sign. : _____

☆ ☆ ☆ ☆ ☆

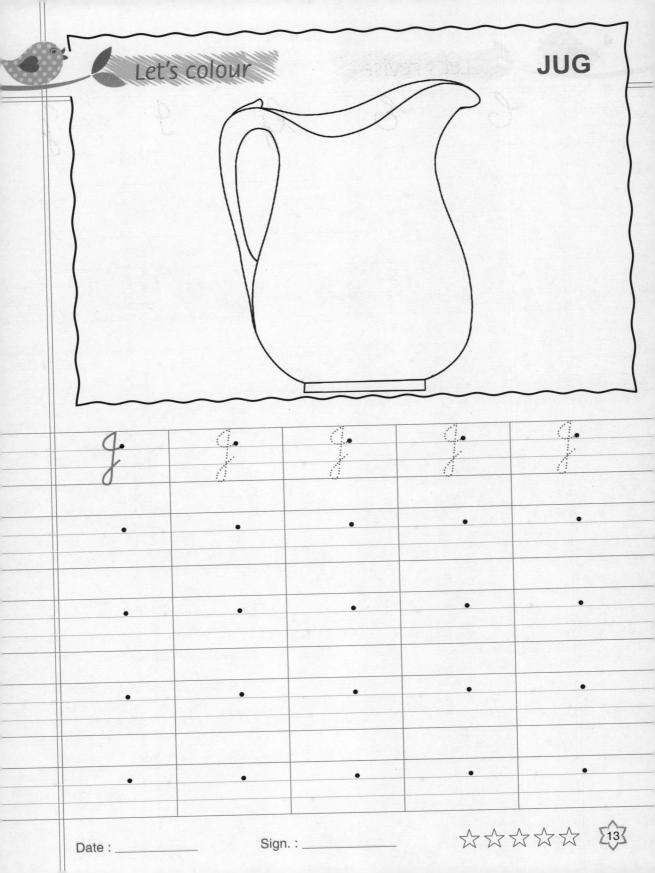

Let's colour

JUG

C   E   G   I   J

Date : _____   Sign. : _____   ☆☆☆☆☆

Circle the odd one

E   E   C   E   E

J   J   J   g   J

G   G   G   G   E

J   g   g   g   g

Date : _____   Sign. : _____   ☆☆☆☆☆

Now, write the letter P .

Date : _____   Sign. : _____   ☆★★★☆

Let's colour

PEACOCK

P   P   P   P   P

Date : _____   Sign. : _____   ☆☆☆☆☆   17

BUTTERFLY

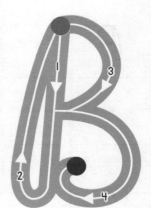

Now, write the letter $\mathcal{B}$.

Date : _____   Sign. : _____   ☆☆☆☆☆

Let's colour

BALL

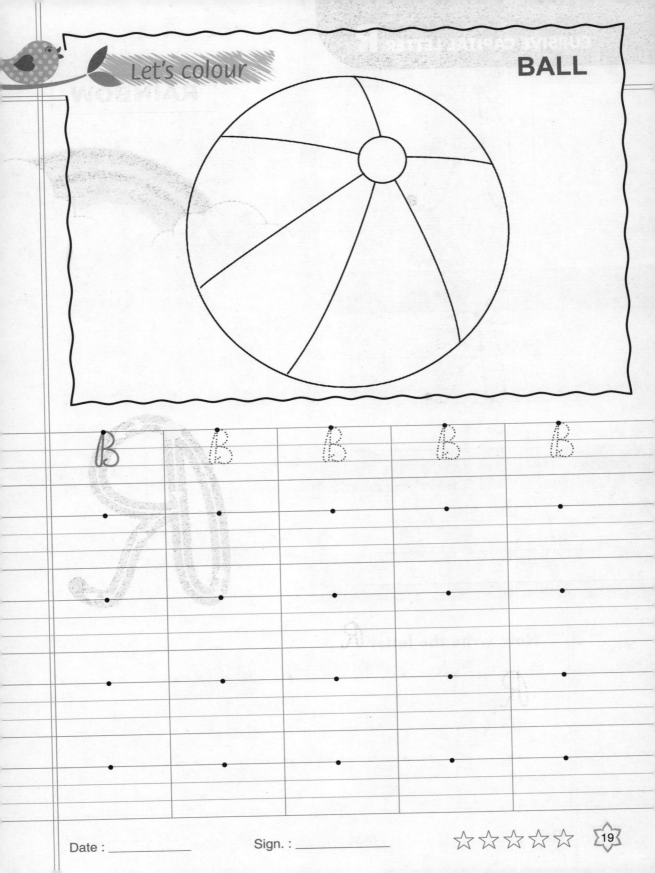

B   B   B   B   B

Date : _____   Sign. : _____   ☆☆☆☆☆

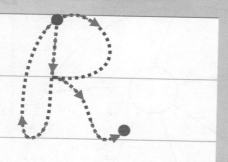

RAINBOW

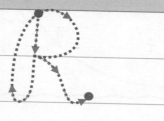

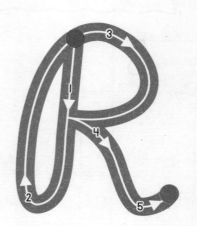

Now, write the letter $\mathcal{R}$ **.**

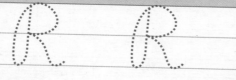

Date : _____   Sign. : _____   ☆☆☆☆☆

RAT

R R R R R

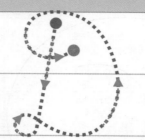

DRUM

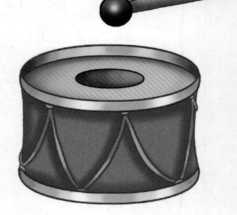

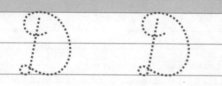

Now, write the letter 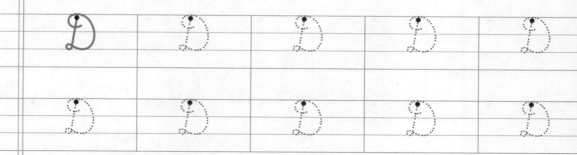 **.**

Date : _____   Sign. : _____   ☆☆☆☆☆

DOG

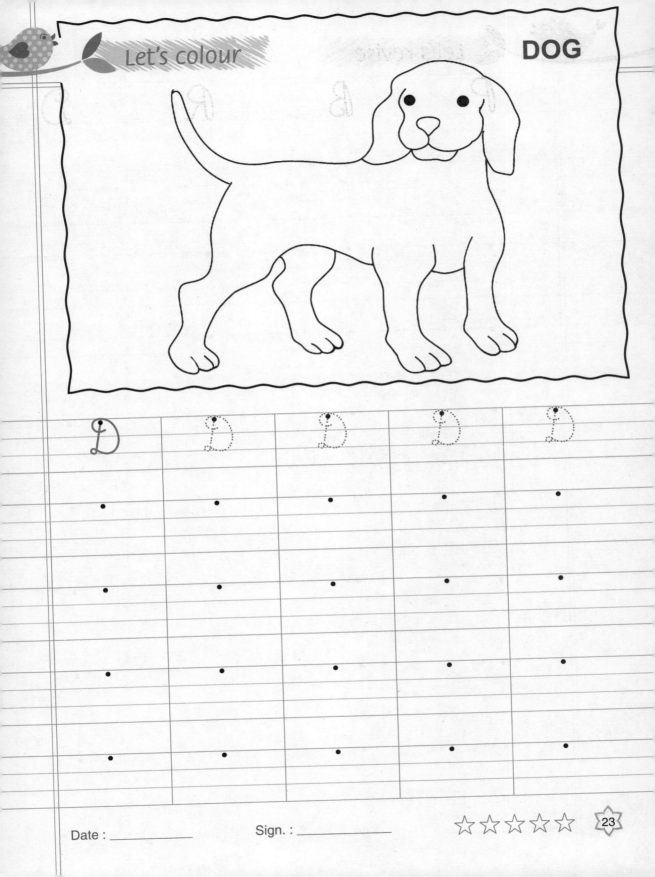

D

Date : _____

Sign. : _____

P   B   R   D

P   B   R   D

P   B   R   D

Date : _____   Sign. : _____   ☆☆☆☆☆

Match the letter to the picture

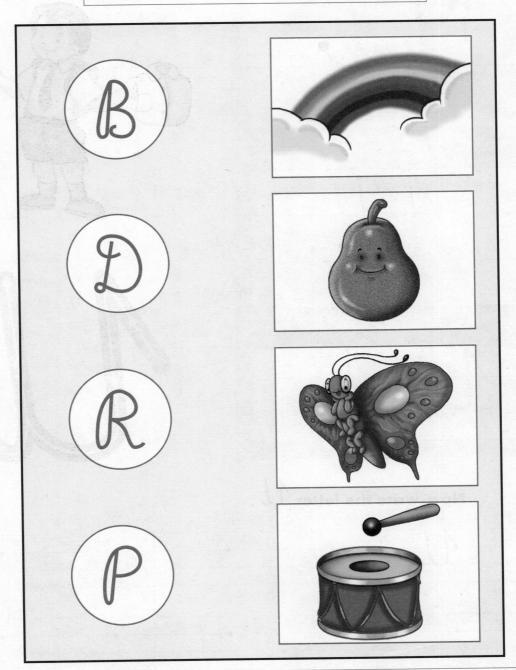

UNIFORM

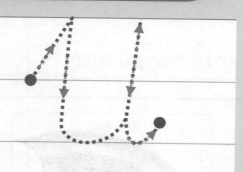

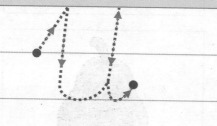

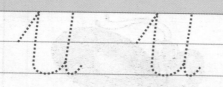

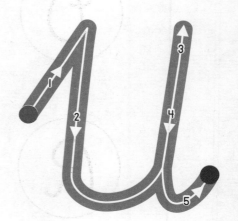

Now, write the letter $\mathcal{U}$.

Date : _____   Sign. : _____   ☆ ☆ ☆ ☆ ☆

Let's colour

UMBRELLA

u   u   u   u   u

Date : _____ Sign. : _____ ☆☆☆☆☆

VIOLIN

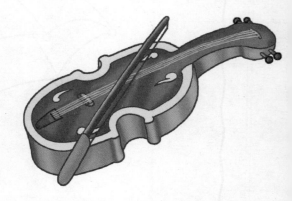

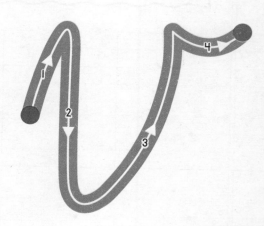

Now, write the letter $\mathcal{V}$ **.**

Date : _____   Sign. : _____   ☆☆☆☆☆

Let's colour

VAN

Date : _____   Sign. : _____   ☆☆☆☆☆ 29

WOMAN

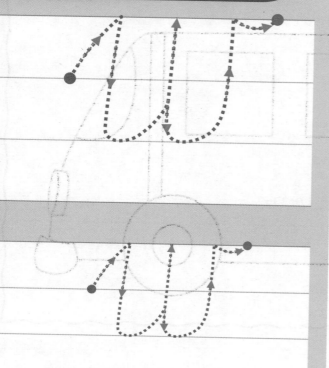

Now, write the letter *W* .

Date : _____   Sign. : _____

Let's colour

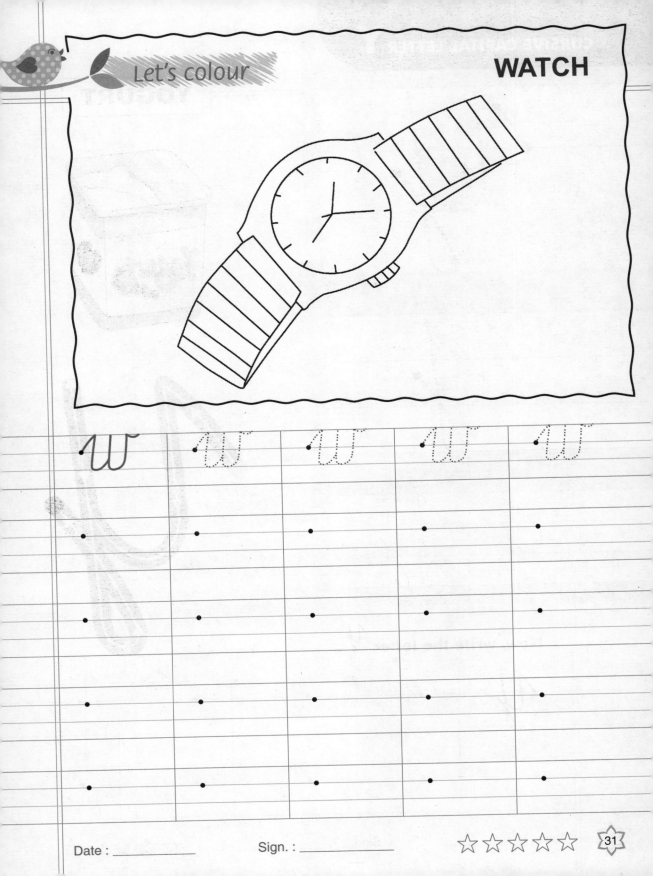

W

Date : _____   Sign. : _____

YOGURT

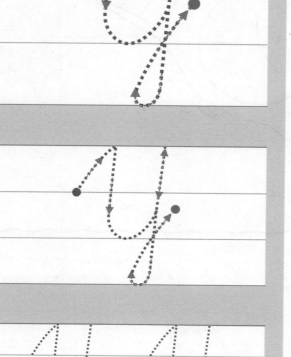

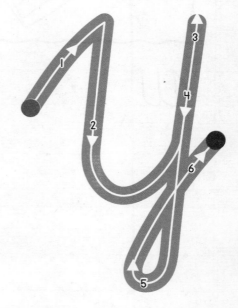

Now, write the letter $\mathcal{Y}$.

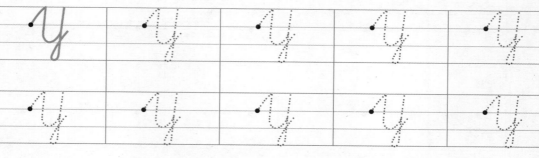

Date : _____   Sign. : _____   ☆☆☆☆☆

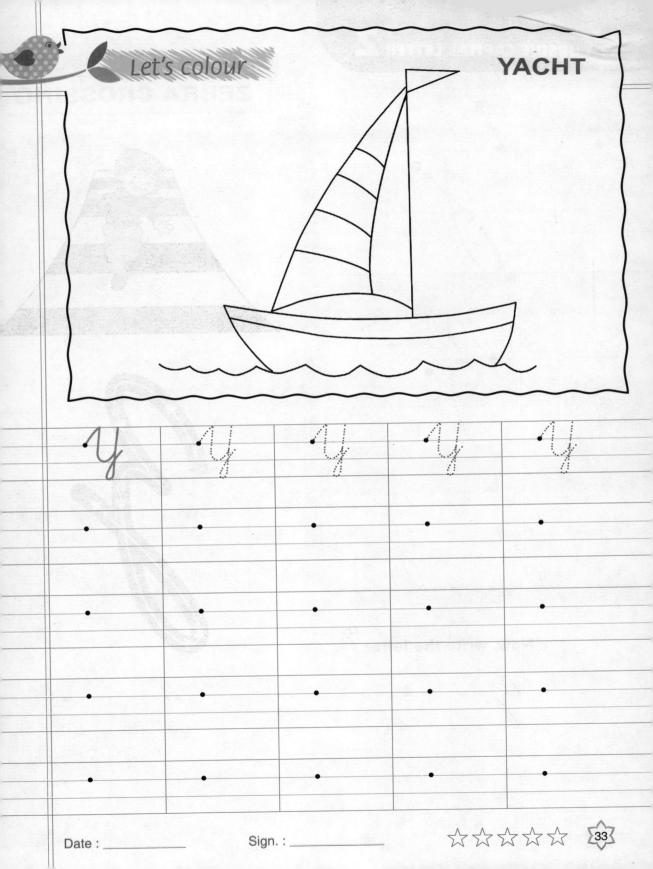

Y   Y   Y   Y   Y

Date : _____   Sign. : _____   ☆☆☆☆☆

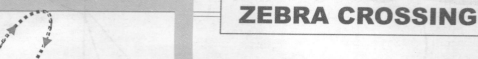

ZEBRA CROSSING

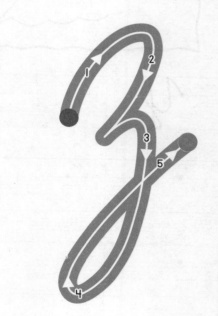

Now, write the letter 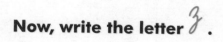 **.**

Date : _____   Sign. : _____

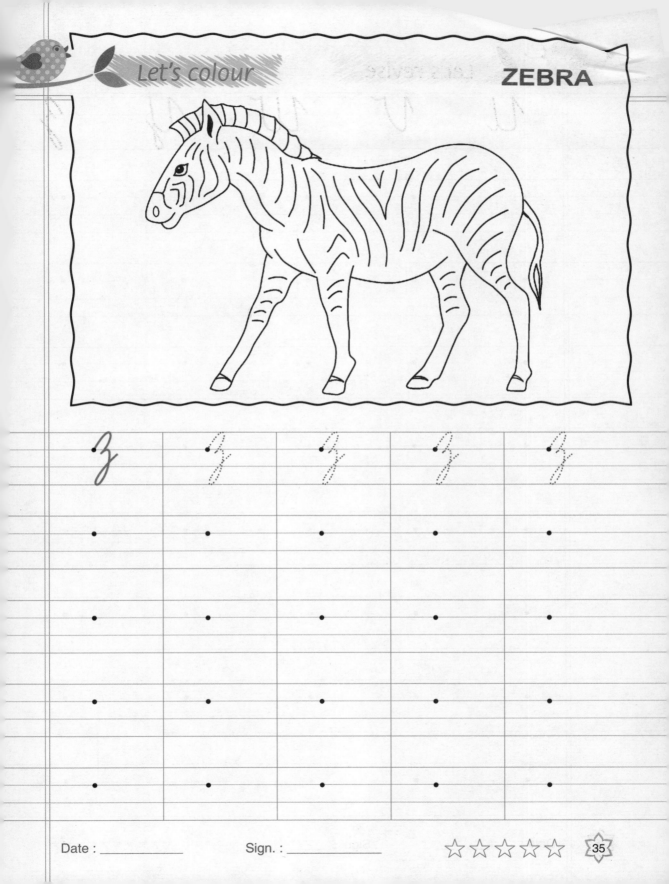

u v w y z

u v w y z

u v w y z

Date : _____   Sign. : _____   ☆☆☆☆☆

Join the pictures with their first letter

Write the first letter of the picture

Date : _____   Sign. : _____   ☆ ☆ ☆ ☆ ☆

E   E   ly   I   I

P   B   R   D

U   V   W   Y   Z

Date : _____   Sign. : _____   ☆☆☆☆☆ 39

OCTOPUS

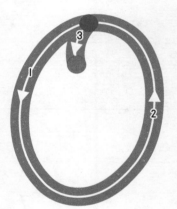

Now, write the letter O **.**

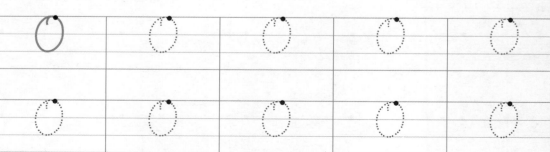

Date : _____   Sign. : _____   ☆☆☆☆☆

Let's colour

OWL

Date : _____   Sign. : _____   ☆☆☆☆☆   41

QUEUE

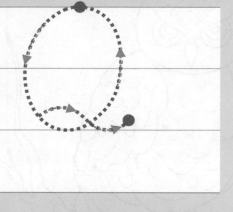

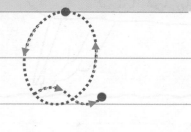

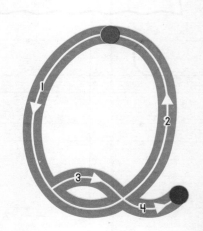

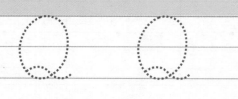

Now, write the letter Q.

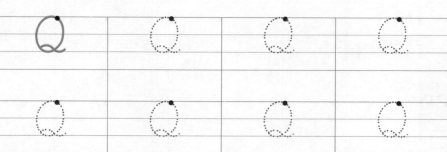

Date : _____   Sign. : _____   ☆☆☆☆☆

Let's colour

QUEEN

Q

X-MAS TREE

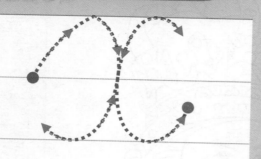

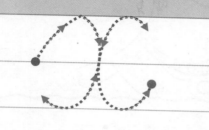

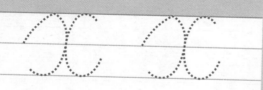

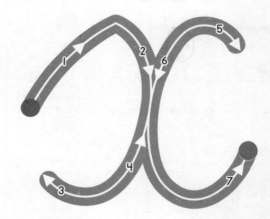

Now, write the letter 𝒳 **.**

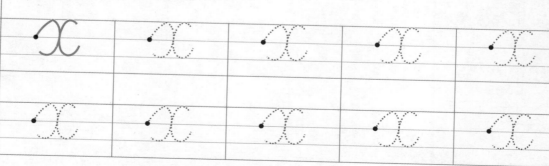

Date : _____   Sign. : _____   ☆☆☆☆☆

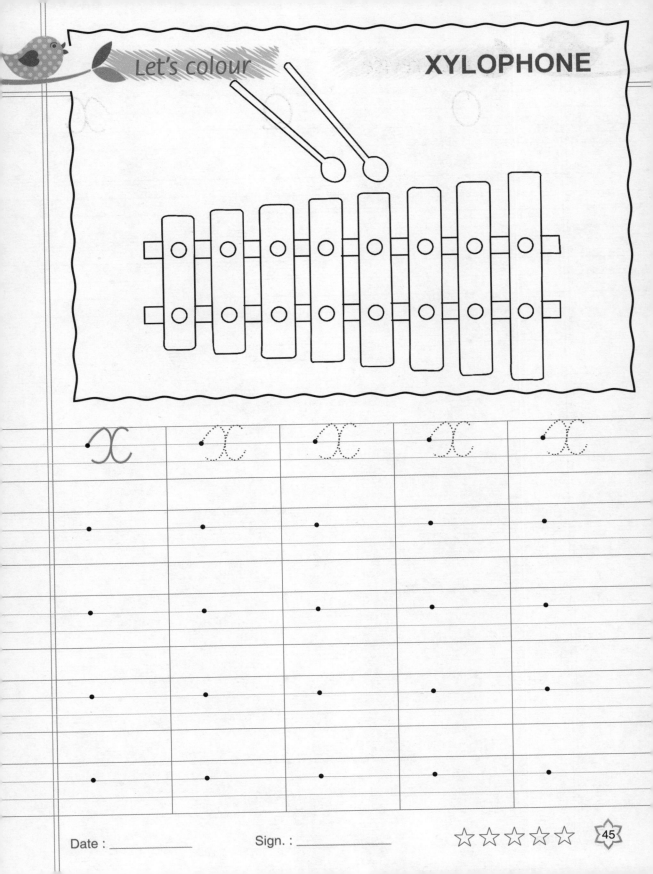

Date : _____　　　Sign. : _____

O　　Q　　X

Date : _____　　Sign. : _____　　☆☆☆☆☆

Let's practice

Trace all 'O'

Trace all 'Q'

Trace all 'X'

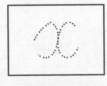   

Date : _____   Sign. : _____   ☆☆☆☆☆   47

TOMATO

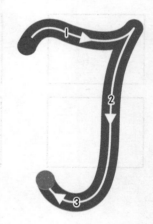

Now, write the letter $\mathcal{T}$.

Date : _____   Sign. : _____   ☆☆☆☆☆

Let's colour

TIGER

J J J J J

FLOWER

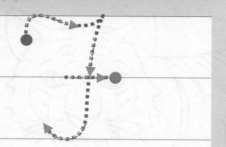

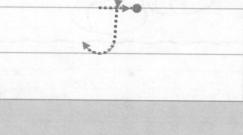

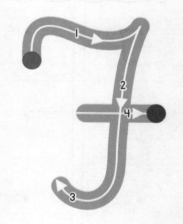

Now, write the letter $\mathcal{F}$.

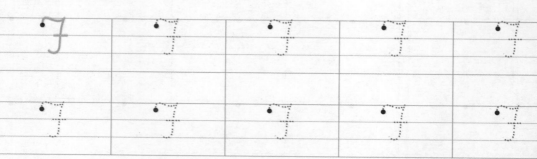

Date : _____

Sign. : _____

☆☆☆☆☆

Let's colour

FLAG

Date : _____ Sign. : _____ ☆☆☆☆☆

HAMMER

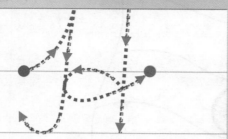

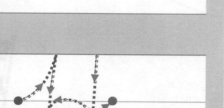

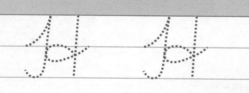

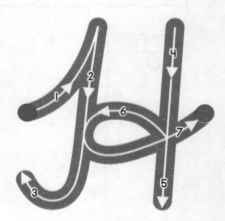

Now, write the letter $\mathcal{H}$.

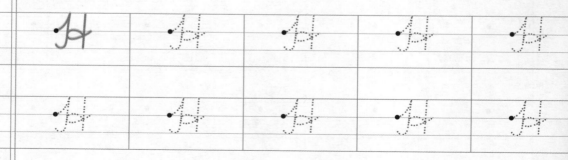

Date : _____   Sign. : _____   ☆☆☆☆☆

HORSE

H H H H H

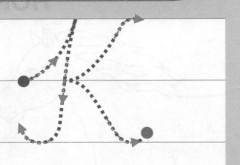

KETTLE

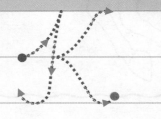

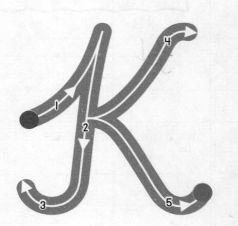

Now, write the letter $\mathcal{K}$.

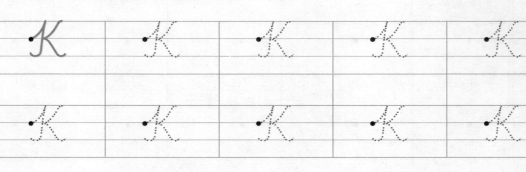

Date : _____   Sign. : _____   ☆ ☆ ☆ ☆ ☆

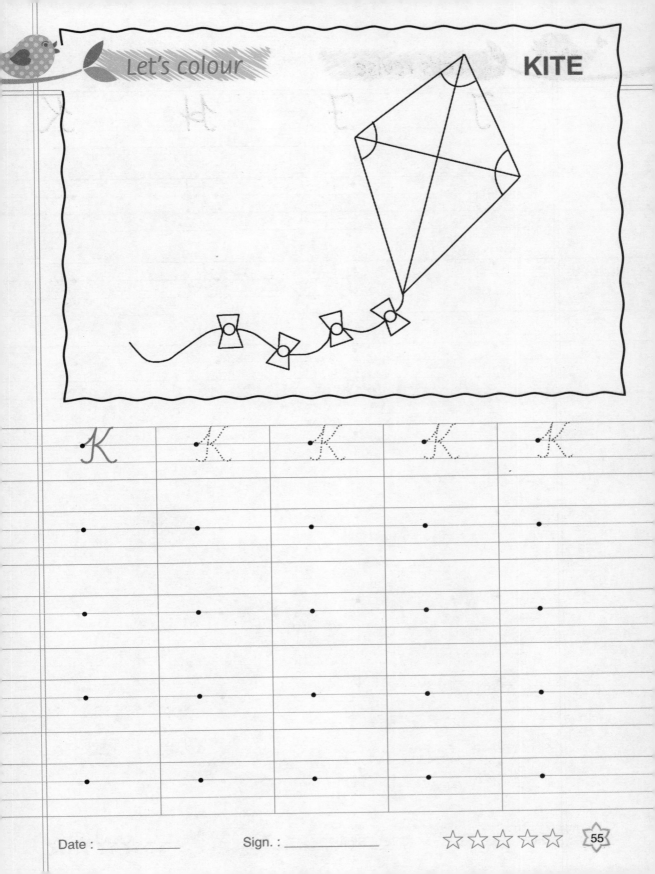

Let's colour

KITE

K   K   K   K   K

Date : _____   Sign. : _____

$J \qquad F \qquad H \qquad K$

$J \qquad F \qquad H \qquad K$

$J \qquad F \qquad H \qquad K$

Date : _____   Sign. : _____   ☆☆☆☆☆

Let's practice

See the pictures and encircle the first letter

$\mathcal{J}$ $\mathcal{T}$ $\mathcal{B}$

$\mathcal{H}$ $\mathcal{G}$ $\mathcal{D}$

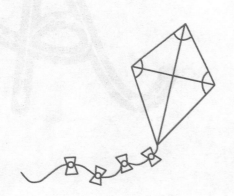

$\mathcal{K}$ $\mathcal{Z}$ $\mathcal{P}$

$\mathcal{R}$ $\mathcal{Y}$ $\mathcal{F}$

Date : _____   Sign. : _____

☆☆☆☆☆

ANGEL

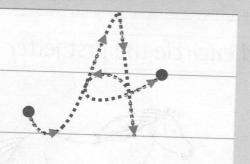

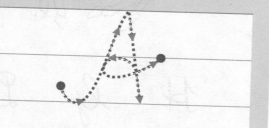

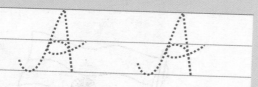

Now, write the letter 𝒜.

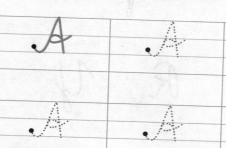

Date : _____

Sign. : _____

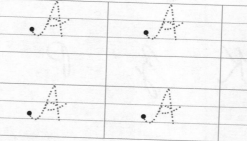

Let's colour

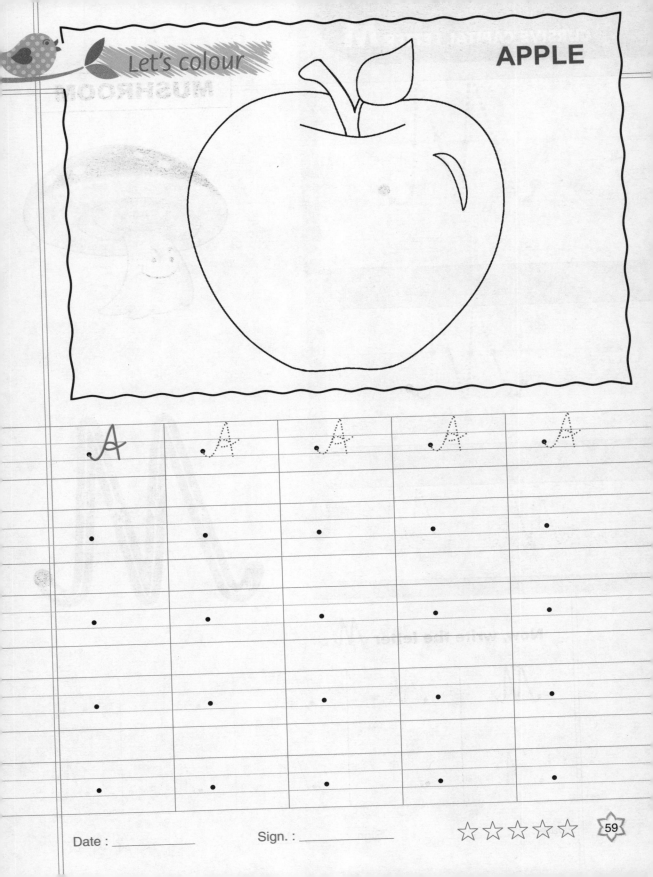

Date : _____   Sign. : _____

MUSHROOM

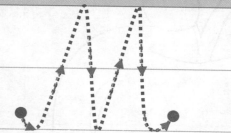

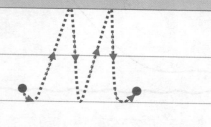

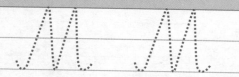

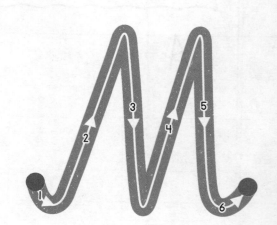

Now, write the letter $\mathcal{M}$.

$\mathcal{M}$	$\mathcal{M}$	$\mathcal{M}$	$\mathcal{M}$	$\mathcal{M}$
$\mathcal{M}$	$\mathcal{M}$	$\mathcal{M}$	$\mathcal{M}$	$\mathcal{M}$

Date : _____   Sign. : _____   ☆ ☆ ☆ ☆ ☆

Let's colour

MANGO

Date : _____   Sign. : _____

NOSE

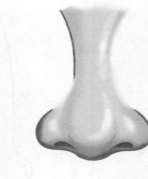

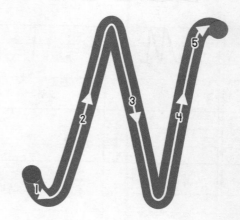

Now, write the letter $\mathcal{N}$.

Date : _____   Sign. : _____   ☆☆☆☆☆

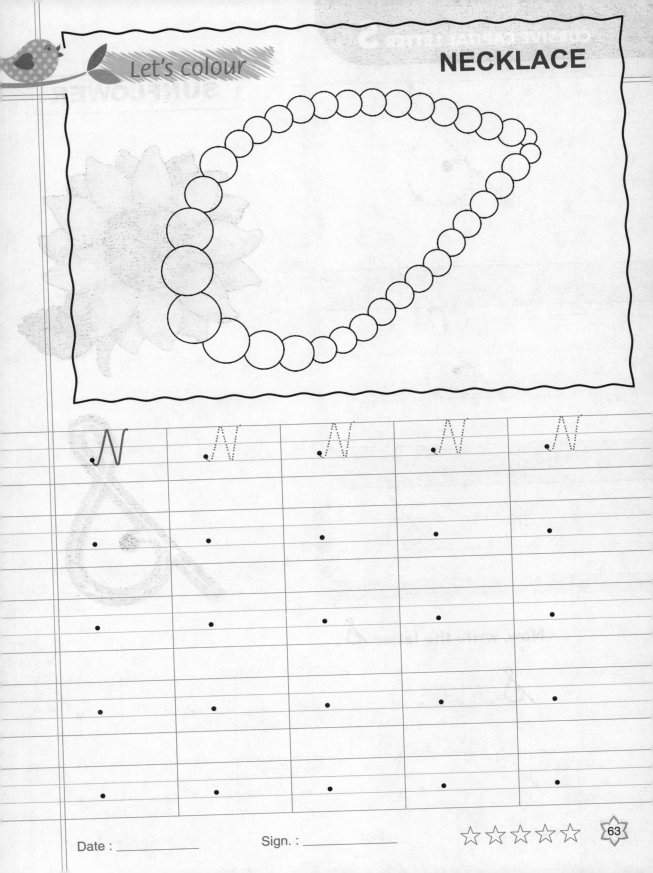

Let's colour

NECKLACE

Date : _____

Sign. : _____

SUNFLOWER

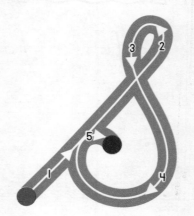

Now, write the letter $\mathcal{S}$.

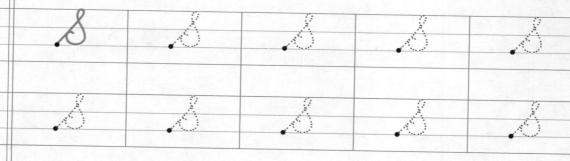

Date : _____   Sign. : _____   ☆☆☆☆☆

Let's colour

SUN

LAMP

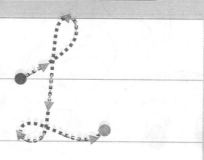

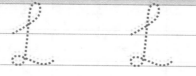

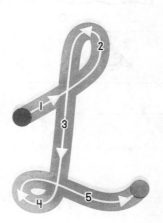

Now, write the letter $\mathcal{L}$.

Date : _____   Sign. : _____   ☆ ☆ ☆ ☆ ☆

LOCK

Date : _____   Sign. : _____

Let's revise

A M N S L

A M N S L

A M N S L

Date : _____   Sign. : _____   ☆☆☆☆☆

68

Match the letter to the picture

C   E   G   I   J

P   B   R   D

U   V   W   Y   Z

Date : _____   Sign. : _____   ☆☆☆☆☆

O   Q   X

J   F   H   K

A   M   N   S   L

Date : _____   Sign. : _____

A   B   C   D

E   F   G   H

I   J   K   L

M   N   O   P

Q   R   S   T

U   V   W   X

Y   Z

Date : _____   Sign. : _____   ☆ ☆ ☆ ☆ ☆

𝒜

ℨ

Date : _____   Sign. : _____   ☆☆☆☆☆

Fill in the blanks

A   C

_____   _____

         F   H

_____   _____

I   L

_____   _____

        N   O

_____   _____

        R

_____   _____

           W

_____   _____   _____

Y

_____

Date : _____   Sign. : _____   ☆☆☆☆☆

Write the first letter of the picture

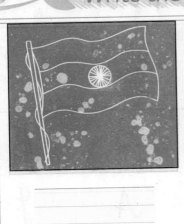

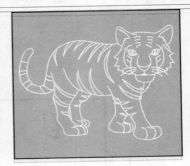

_____

_____

_____

_____

_____

_____

_____

_____

_____

Date : _____   Sign. : _____   75

Colour the boxes as shown below

A		Z	

H	E	A	G	B
I	A	O	A	I
A	N	Z	S	A
A	Z	F	Z	A
A	Z	L	Z	A
A	Z	U	Z	A
A	Q	Z	P	A
K	A	R	A	M
K	A	R	A	M
C	H	A	F	D

Date : _____   Sign. : _____   ☆☆☆☆☆

Let's play

Follow A to Z and help the boy to reach his home

A	B	C	D	E	M
I	S	F	E	G	A
U	R	G	F	K	D
V	Q	H	I	J	P
W	P	W	O	K	L
X	O	N	M	L	R
Y	A	B	C	G	S
Z	N	M	Q	F	I

Date : _____   Sign. : _____   ☆☆☆☆☆

A B C

Lovely morning to see.

D E F

You have slept enough.

G H I

Never tell a lie.

J K L

Do not yell.

M N O

Learn and grow.

Date : _____   Sign. : _____   ☆ ☆ ☆ ☆ ☆

Shine like a star.

That's beautiful you.

Try to be the best.

Smart you should be.

Start from **A** and stop at **Z**

Date : _____   Sign. : _____   ☆☆☆☆☆